Missing!

Alison Hawes • **Jon Stuart**

Contents

Welcome to Micro World! .... page 2

Bug Facts .... page 5

Slip Up .... page 13

OXFORD
UNIVERSITY PRESS

Macro Marvel
(billionaire inventor)

Welcome to Micro World!

Macro Marvel invented Micro World – a micro-sized theme park where you have to shrink to get in.

A computer called **CODE** controls Micro World and all the robots inside – MITEs and BITEs.

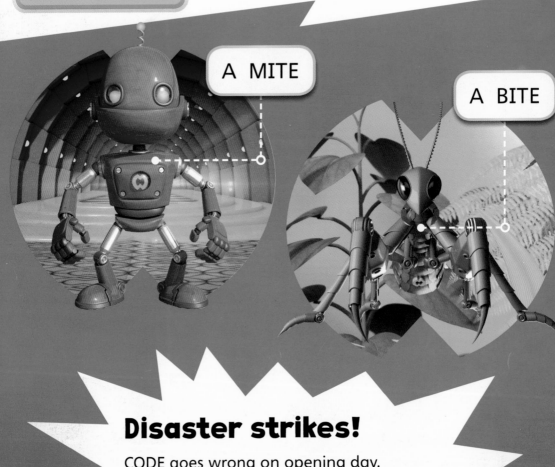

A MITE

A BITE

Disaster strikes!

CODE goes wrong on opening day.
CODE wants to shrink the world.

Macro Marvel is trapped inside the park ...

Enter Team X!

Four micro agents – *Max, Cat, Ant* and *Tiger* – are sent to rescue Macro Marvel and defeat CODE.

Mini Marvel joins Team X.

Mini Marvel
(Macro's daughter)

In the last book ...

* An ant captured Tiger and took him to an ant hill.

* Cat tracked Tiger on her watch.

* Cat helped Tiger to shrink and escape.

CODE key

 You are in the Bugtastic zone.

3

Before you read

Sound checker
Say the sounds.

ch   th
sh   ng

Sound spotter
Blend the sounds.

th	i	s

sh	e	ll

s	l	u	g

a	l	o	ng

Tricky word

me

Into the zone
Find out all about bugs
with Ant.

4

Bug Facts

Bugs

This moth can shut its wings.

This bug has six legs.

It is red with black dots.

**Buzz!
Buzz!**

This bug buzzes and hums.

It can sting.

It can sting me!

This bug has a shell.

Munch! Munch!

It munches on plants.

A slug has no legs and no shell.

It slips along on its track.

A mantis has wings and long thin legs.

It can grab and pinch its victims.

Now you have read ...
Bug Facts

Text checker
Which label goes with which picture?

moth	snail
mantis	slug
bee	ladybird

MITE fun
What can a mantis do?

Watch out for me!

11

Before you read

Sound checker

Say the sounds.

ch   th
sh   ng

Sound spotter

Blend the sounds.

m	i	ss	i	ng

d	a	sh

ch	e	ck

th	u	m	p

Tricky words

we
me
be

Into the zone

Cat and Tiger are missing.
Will Team X and Mini
find them?

Slip Up

Team X must get the CODE key
but Tiger and Cat are missing.
Max, Ant and Mini go to find them.

They dash along the path.

Cat!

Tiger!

They check in the bushes.

They are in such a rush!
They skid on the slug track.
Thump!

Max steps on a stick!

crunch!

We must go back.

Follow me!

They dash back.
They run past the slug tracks.

The BITE can not see the slug tracks. Crash!
It lands on its back.

The BITE can not get up.
The MITEs help it.

Max, Ant and Mini rush back to the Big Bug. They see Cat and Tiger.

They are not missing after all.

Now you have read ...
Slip Up

Crunch!
Thump!
Crash!

Text checker
Match the sound with the picture.

MITE fun
What sound did the stick make when Max stepped on it?

I am stuck!